r is for rabbit

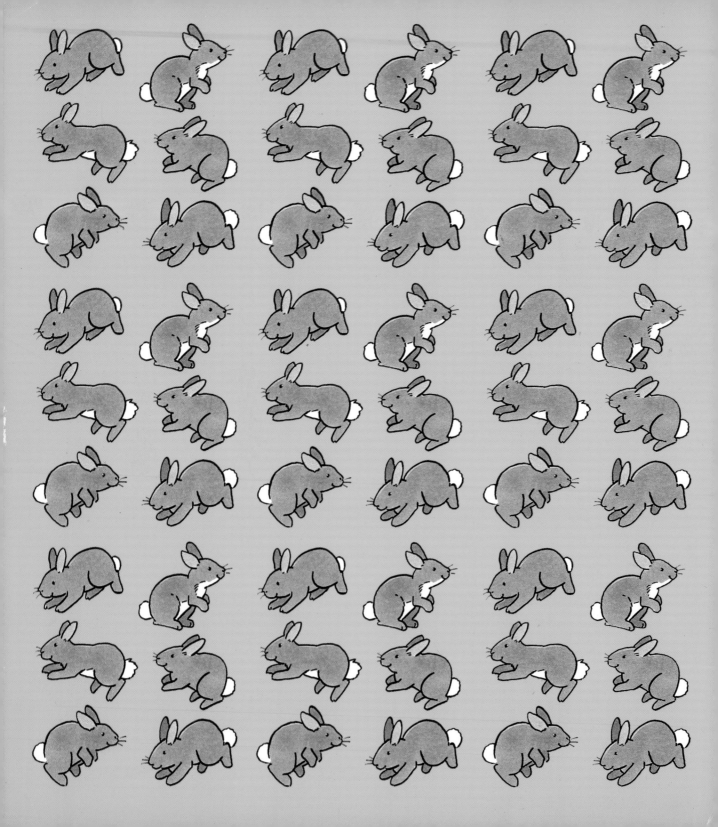

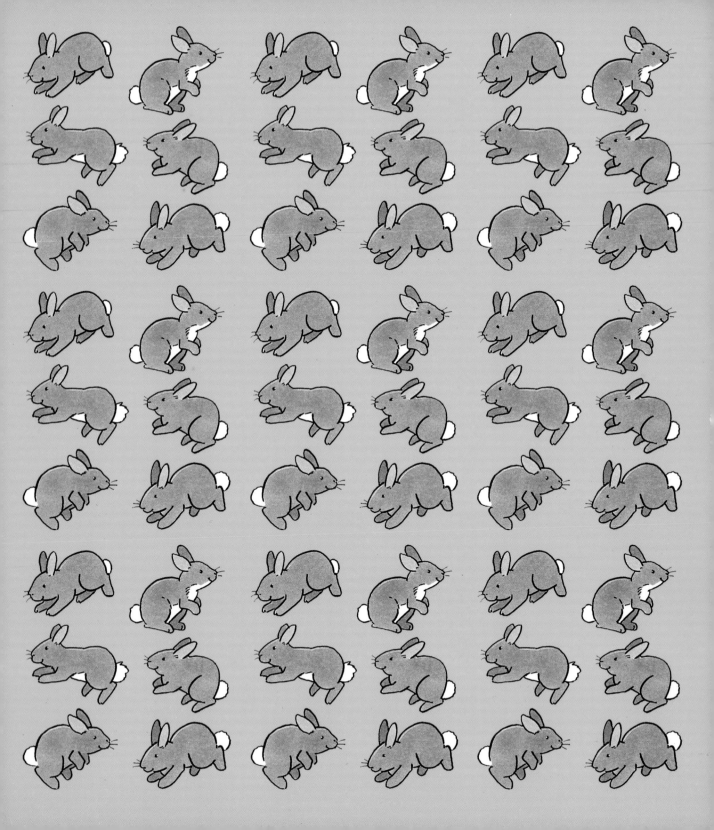

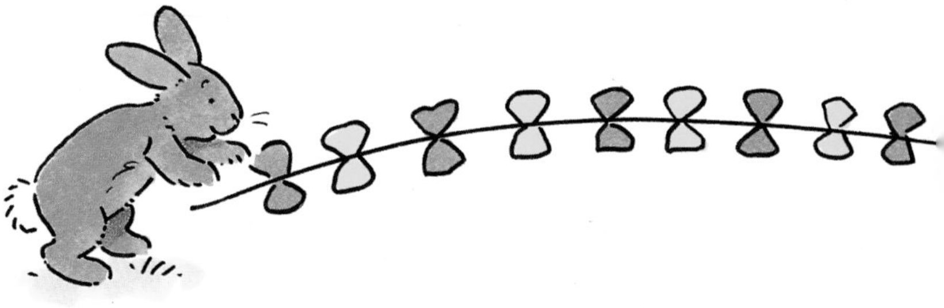

A Flip The Flap Book

r is for rabbit

Richard Powell
Illustrated by Stuart Trotter

t is for

h is for

p is for

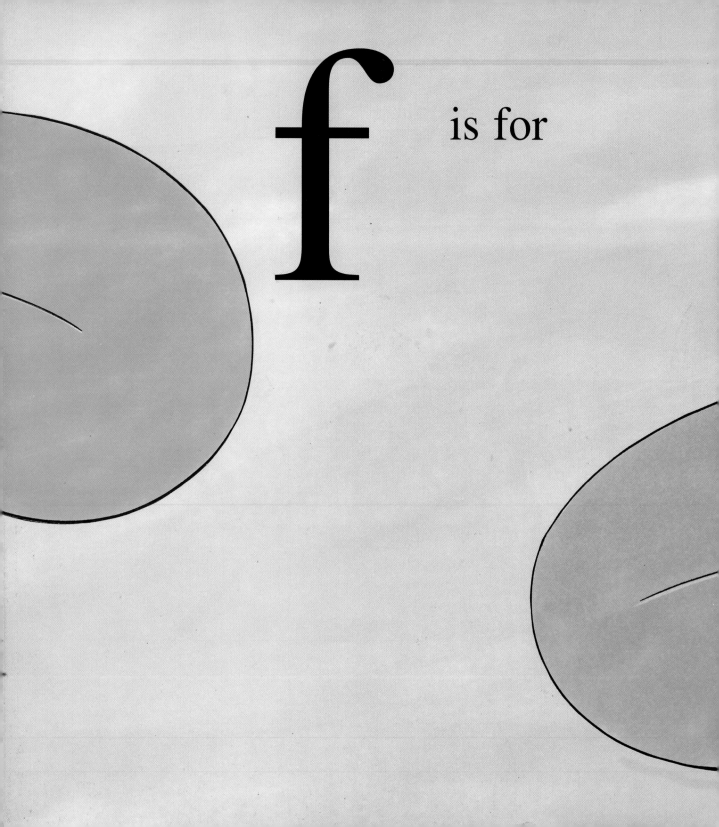

f is for

W is for

d is for

the

n is for

r is for

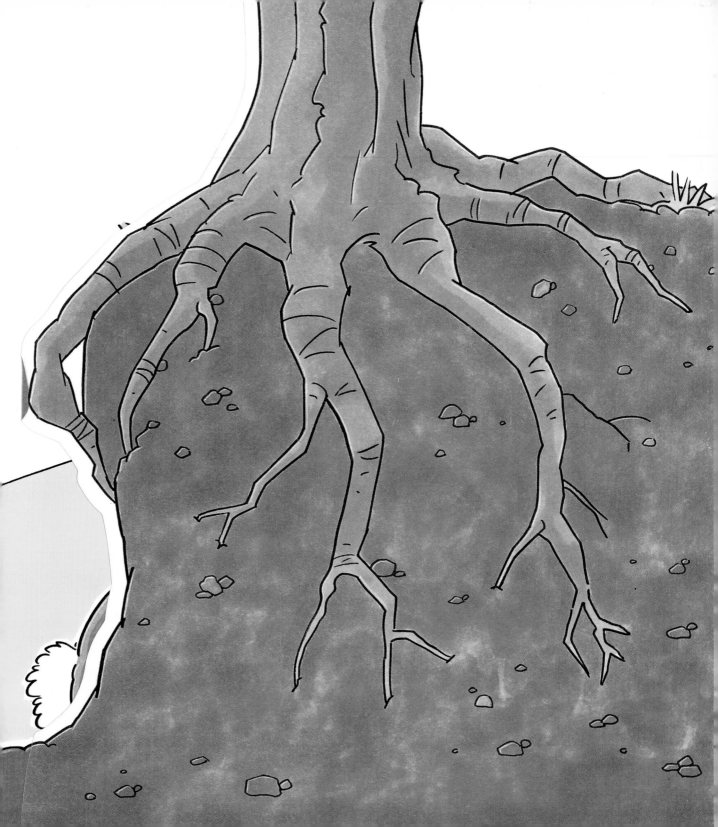

S is for

b is for the

g is for

C is for

the countryside

all around.

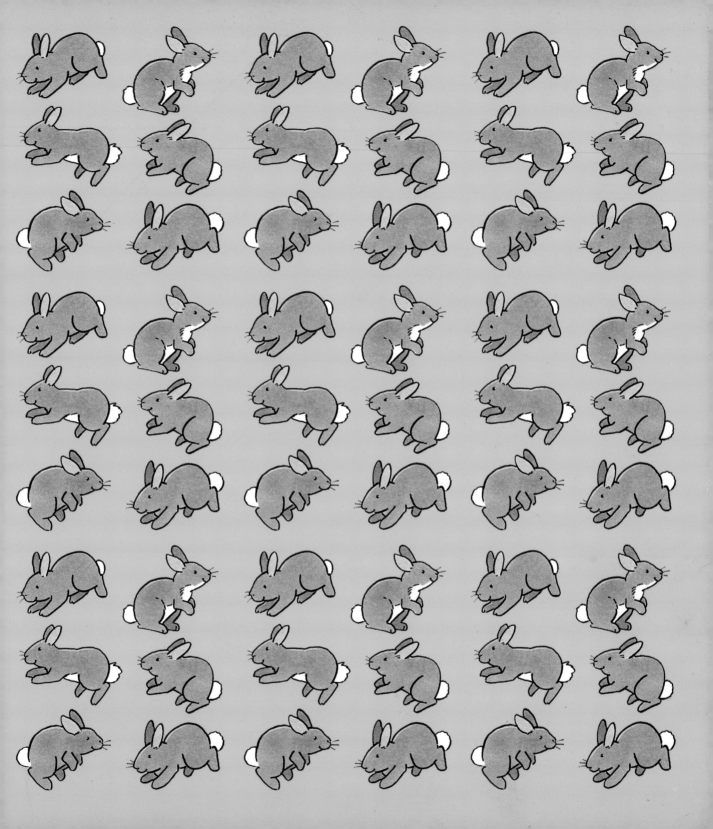